Contemporary Classics
The Vidal Sassoon Way, Volume 2

Published by
Haircare Limited, 56 Brook Street, London, W1Y 1AS, England

FIRST PUBLISHED 1993

ISBN: 0 9519553 1 4

step by step photography by: Angus Ross
Other photography by: Simon Archer, Greg Mason, Peter Mountain/Richard Carroll, Graham Young
Text by Ric Cooper and the Vidal Sassoon Creative Team
designed by: Centurion Design Forum, 2 Kendall Place, London W1H 3AH
printed by: Centurion Press Ltd., 52 George Street, London W1H 5RF

Dear reader, please allow me a moment to talk to you about the British Hairdressers Benevolent and Provident Institution.

The Benevolent, a charitable organisation founded in 1831, provides assistance in cases of need to current and ex hairdressers and their dependents in the U.K.
During the current decade, requests for financial help are increasing fast requiring a major fund raising programme to be undertaken.
The Vidal Sassoon Salons and Schools group is pleased to continue its support of the Benevolent, by donating £1 from every sale of this book.
If you would like to find out more about how you can help please contact:

Secretary, the Benevolent, Phoenix House, 211-213B, High Road, Benfleet, Essex SS7 5HZ England

Thank you for your support and in turn I hope this book will give you many years of satisfaction.
Yours sincerely

Phillip Rogers Managing Director

CONTENTS

It is a source of great personal pride to me that the organisation I founded so many years ago continues to provide inspiration and practical help to hairdressers all over the world.

The sharing of knowledge, the encouragement of talent, and total commitment to training – these are the tenets to which we have always held, and the reason our creative teams continue to dominate fashion haircutting, colouring and perming.

With the publication of this second volume of "Contemporary Classics" hairdressers can continue the learning process: practising and perfecting the techniques demonstrated, and fine tuning their own creative instincts.

May I take this opportunity to wish you all every success in your continuing career.

Vidal Sassoon LONDON, 1993.

WELCOME BACK

How exciting to be welcoming you to Volume Two of "Contemporary Classics" just a short time after the publication of Volume One. Your response has been overwhelming, and we're sure that this sequel matches its companion for excitement and professionalism every step of the way.

As you will see, the Vidal Sassoon Creative Team have once again been busy designing and perfecting a further five new looks to see us into the new millenium, four for women, and one for men, each explained and demonstrated with detailed descriptions and plentiful pinsharp photography.

Remember that in conjunction with the "Contemporary Classics" video series, these two books now form the basis for a complete in-salon training programme like no other ever developed.

As before, we have assumed that our readers have already mastered basic hairdressing skills, ideally by attending Vidal Sassoon courses at one of our international training centres around the world. You will find details of these at the end of the book.

If you can learn to apply yourself and your creative skills with the same care and precision which have made Vidal Sassoon the premier name in hairdressing, then our efforts will have been worthwhile. And never forget the key: practise makes perfect. Have a great time.

Annie Humphreys
Director of Colour and Technical Research

Tim Hartley
International Creative Director

To pursue a career as a creative artist is, by its very nature, an exceptional act; something outside normal experience, something to which only your heart and your talent can lead you.

Whether a chef, a designer, an architect or a hairdresser, the same disciplines apply: application, attention to detail, and continuous, rigorous practise.

Just occasionally a star may shoot across the firmament without all or any of these strengths to their name; but without application, without personal progression, their fate is quickly sealed: the highest ground has always belonged to the artist who lives to work, and who brings a philosophy of excellence to every aspect of his or her daily life.

Today's hairdresser is no exception. The pressures of running a business, of recruiting and organising staff, of dealing with the thousand-and-one things that conspire to keep you apart from your scissors, will slowly debilitate even the most diligent talent.

So how can you stay fresh? If senior how can you continue to lead and inspire those around you? How can you retain the loyalty of those customers who form the core of your business? And if at the start of your career, how can you keep the momentum going and retain the enthusiasm which has brought you to this point?

The answers already lie within you. Beginning with a personal commitment to the pursuit of excellence in your craft, you must learn to extend that vision, and seek to apply it at every opportunity.

Try to reflect the care and precision you employ when cutting hair in other areas of your experience: the way you look, the way you communicate, the food you eat, the relationships you enjoy.

The satisfaction of knowing that you are striving to be not just a good hairdresser, but a consistently better one, will be amplified tenfold by pursuing excellence for its own sake in other aspects of your life.

For those among you who already manage your own hairdressing business, retaining the creative drive is still harder: running a successful salon is a difficult job. It carries no passengers and is slow to forgive laxness or improvisation. Vidal Sassoon salons succeed because our legendary precision is applied to every possible detail of the workplace as well as the actual haircut, from the lighting, to the towels, to the coffee we serve.

But your chief concern should always be your staff. How did you recruit them? How did you recognise they had what it takes? Did you train each and every one of them in your philosophy, and your techniques? If not, there may be negative forces simmering, "accidents waiting to happen", preventing the harmony and atmosphere of trust so essential for the perfect working environment.

Ask yourself, is your salon a happy place, where familiar clients and new customers are treated with equal politeness and genuine respect? Or are you sometimes aware of your staff chatting away to each other, instead of to their clients? Stranded alone in front of that mirror, there is nothing more frustrating and depressing than to be ignored or patronised by the very person you are paying to give you the best possible attention.

And what of the total service you provide? Are you providing the right technical support, as well as psychological reassurance? Your client has only an hour or two with you, perhaps once a month. Is your advice being followed as it should be, backed up by the right products and routines?

At Vidal Sassoon we have a science-led approach to product formulation which has led to the introduction of the Vidal Sassoon Professional Collection. This range is only available through salons, and will keep your client's hair in the best possible condition at all times.

And finally, the craft itself...and at Vidal Sassoon it's always "the cut that counts" – the cut that embodies everything we believe about precision, about training, and about being the best.

Vidal Sassoon-trained hairdressers know it means checking, cross checking, and then checking again to make sure your cutting is accurate, crisp, perfect.

Good cutting is at the heart of all five of the looks we demonstrate in this book, and the only way to achieve it is by constant practise and attention to detail.

Try to keep an even dampness throughout the cut – don't work with the hair completely soaking.

*

Move the hair around frequently to check how the look is developing.

*

A Sassoon haircut is all about attention to detail.

ORBIT with DAPPLING COLOUR

A modern classic achieved with use of round graduation to build up structures within a haircut from the underneath upwards. This creates strong yet soft shapes with plenty of volume and elegant movement.

ONE

Begin by checking the hairline carefully for awkward growth patterns, and keep these in mind as you start the cut.
Section off the hair from the temple to the crown, and from this take your first guideline diagonally.

Use the small end of the comb for even tension and overdirect the hair slightly forward to create a graduated edge and a rounded shape.

TWO

Cut this guideline to the desired length.

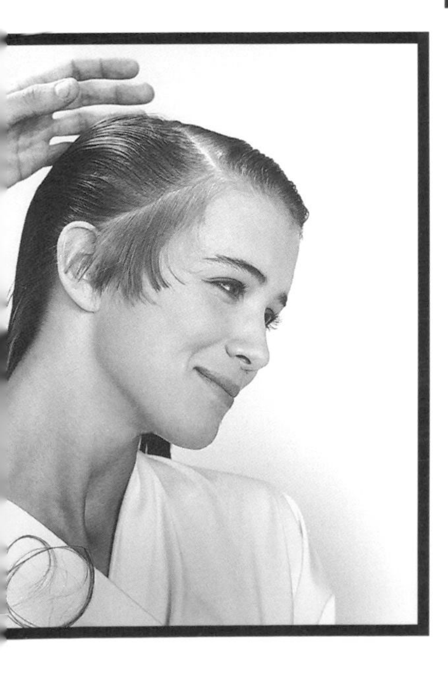

THREE

Now take the second section parallel to the first, creating a curved line from the corner of the eye to the middle of the ear.

Continue taking sections lifting each slightly higher than the previous one to achieve a bevelled internal shape with a graduated edge.

FOUR

The first section behind the ear should be held out a finger's width and angled into the back hairline.

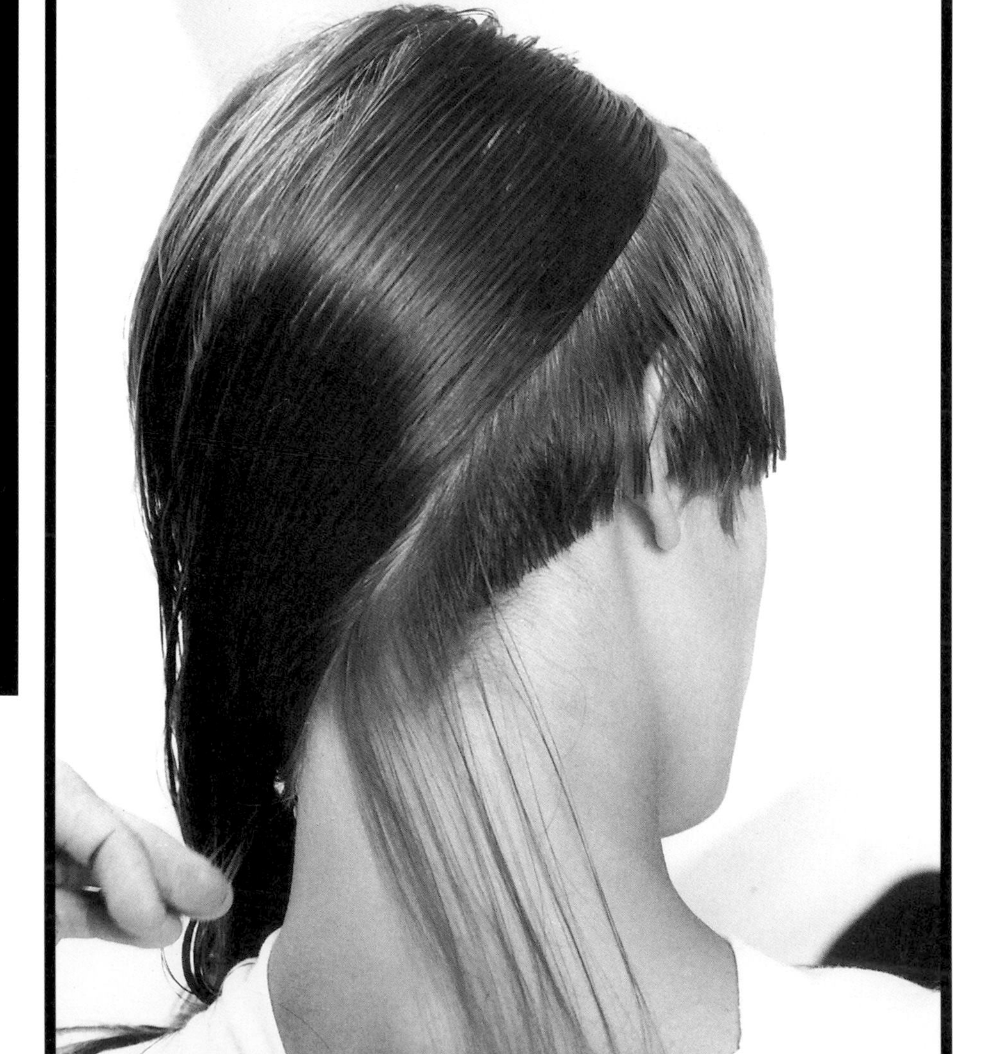

FIVE

Subsequent sections are taken parallel to the previous one and are progressively lifted higher using the previous section as a guide each time.

SIX

Remember to keep the hair an even dampness throughout the cut.

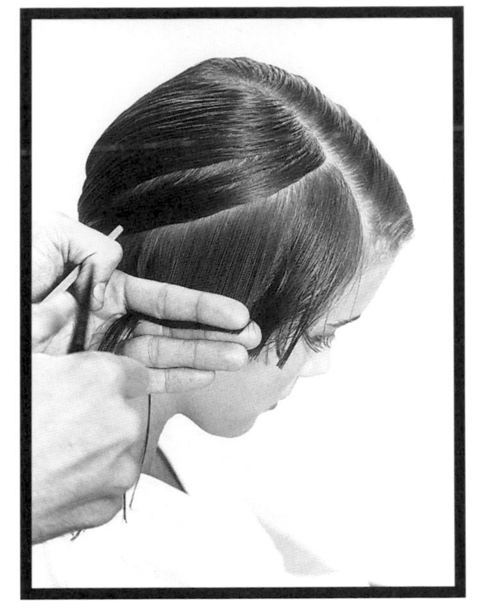

SEVEN

Continue to take sections following the natural contours of the head.

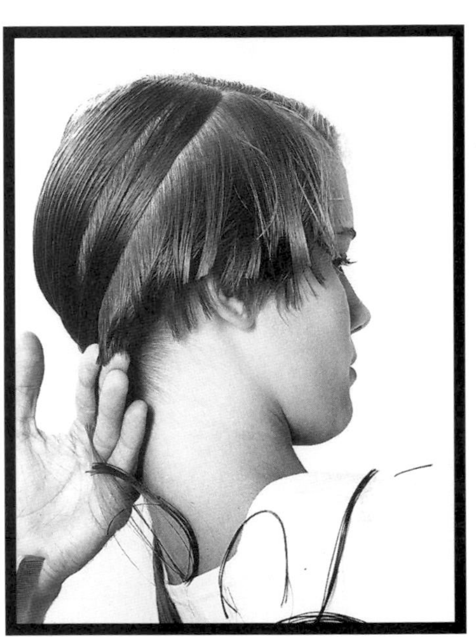

EIGHT

Work the sections at the back into the opposite side, crossing the occipital area and being sure to elevate progressively as you work around the head. Check constantly for visual balance and evenness of graduation.

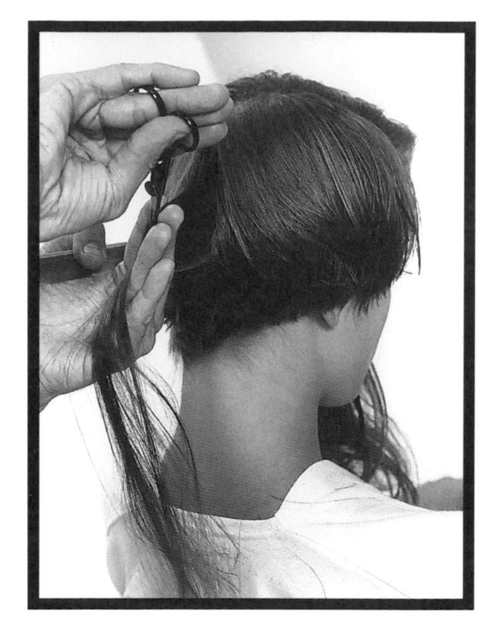

NINE

Continue to work into the opposite side, angling your sections and crossing the occipital area to minimalise any build-up of weight.

TEN

Having completed the first side, take a new parting through the centre of the top of the head. Then take a curved section around the face, connecting with the previously-cut sections.

Hold down to a finger's width to keep weight in the fringe and temple area and cut a curved line, longer towards the front.

ELEVEN

The next section is taken parallel to the first, and lifted slightly; to allow for any thinning in the temple area.

TWELVE

Subsequent sections are lifted progressively higher for continuity of graduation.
N.B. Make sure you keep assessing the shape for visual balance.

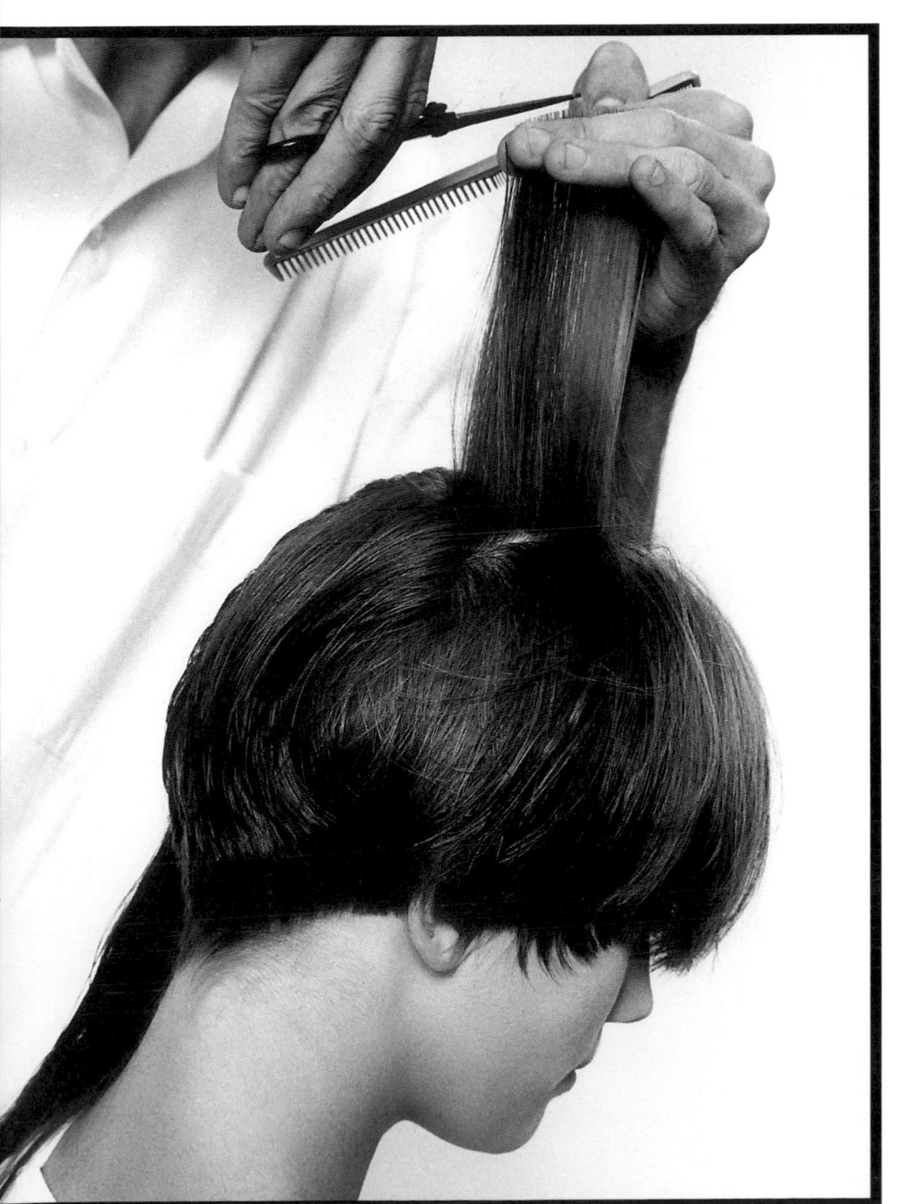

THIRTEEN

Note how the use of round graduation enables you to create this flattering shape.

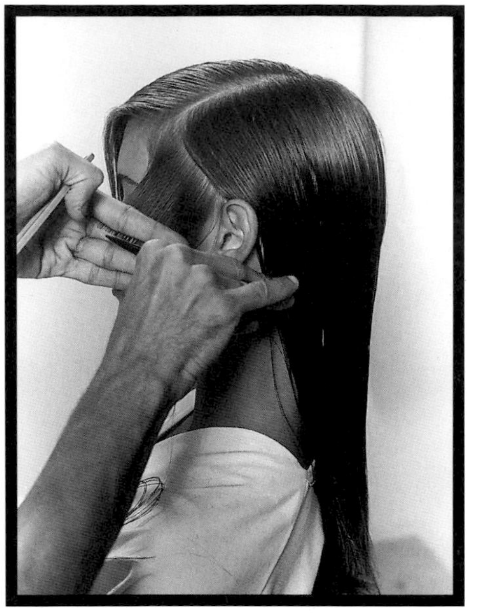

FOURTEEN

The second side is cut exactly the same as the first. Remember to check that you achieve the same length on your guideline, and to overdirect forward slightly to create a graduated shape and a bevelled edge.

FIFTEEN

Once you have completed both sides, approach the fringe area by taking curved sections and joining your existing length at the front to the sides.

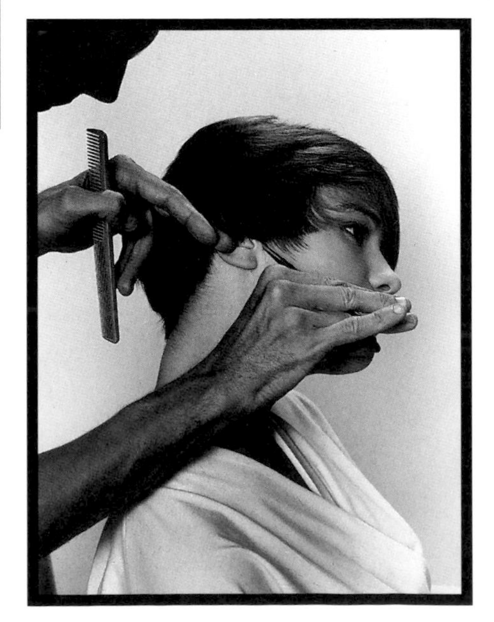

SIXTEEN

Now refine the outline freehand by pointing out any excess length with the tips of the scissors. Be sure to retain a soft edge at the nape by combing the hair down as you point.

Check and check again for consistency of texture and softness.

SEVENTEEN

Apply a suitable finishing product and dry as required.

EIGHTEEN

Your Orbit haircut is now ready for colouring: a striking combination of graceful lines and gentle movement: a simple yet stylish cut designed by The Vidal Sassoon Team.

DAPPLING COLOUR

The Dappling Colour technique is used to create an exciting yet subtle diffusion of colour. Different tints are placed in close proximity so that they blend to create additional textures and hues.

ONE

Take a section from the templcs to below the crown, and check each side is even.

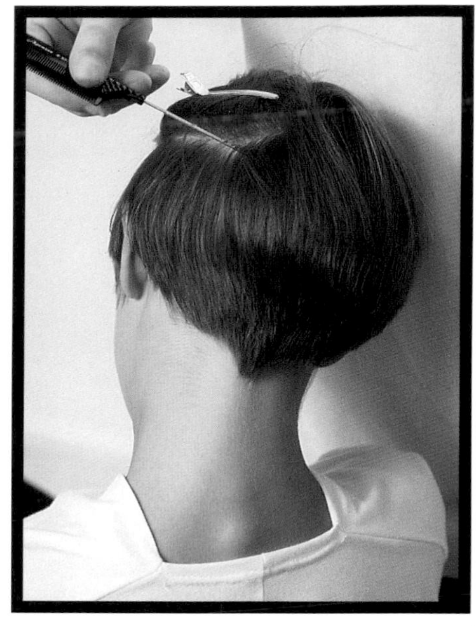

TWO

Now proceed to colour the hair beneath the top section from the centre nape to the front hairline using normal tint application procedure: here the colour used is a hazel brown tint, depth or level 8, with 9% oxidant.

THREE

Because the hair is short, apply the colour from root to tip, combing through after each section to ensure even tint distribution.

FOUR

When you reach the temple area take care to blend the hairline in, to achieve a more natural finish using gentle brush strokes. Place a foil over the areas you have just tinted to separate and protect the underneath sections.

FIVE

Part the hair at the centre top, and take a small diagonal slice: work around the front hairline. Now divide this first section again along its top edge. Place a foil underneath this slice and apply the next colour: a pale blonde, depth or level 10 in a natural shade with 12% oxidant. ***N.B. A slice is a very fine, straight section taken by skimming the surface of the hair with the tail of the comb.***

SIX

Now prepare to apply your next colour: take a perm applicator bottle and pour the colour into it: this is an amber tint, depth or level 7, with NO oxidant. Apply this in a wavelike movement down the length of the original tinted slice, starting from either the left or right hand side at the top.

SEVEN

Now take another applicator bottle, and pour your third colour into this: a red tint, depth or level 8, again with NO oxidant. Apply this tint down the length of the section, again in a wavelike movement, but in the opposite direction from the previous one.

EIGHT

Take a piece of blotting paper, cut to size, and soak it in 6% oxidant. Place this over the applied colours on the section. Gently pat the blotting paper to blend the oxidant in with the colours.

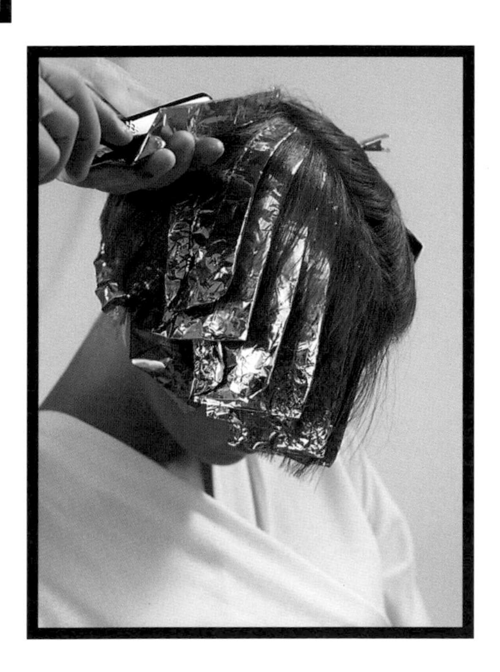

NINE

Continue taking sections, slicing each time along the top edge, leaving some natural hair between the foils. Apply the freehand colours in a wavelike movement as before.
N.B. Remember to close the foils by folding them in half upwards, and then, using your comb, sealing the sides by folding them inwards. This avoids leakage.
Take diagonal sections until you reach the crown area, where you should pivot them vertically so the side sections meet at the centre back.

THE SECOND SIDE.
Take a diagonal section across the front hairline again. Then take a slice and apply a high lift natural blonde tint, depth or level 10 with 12% oxidant. Then apply the freehand colours as before.

Repeat the use of the blotting paper throughout. Continue this through to the centre back.
N.B. It's vital to take diagonal sections so that no separation lines appear when the hair is dressed flat.

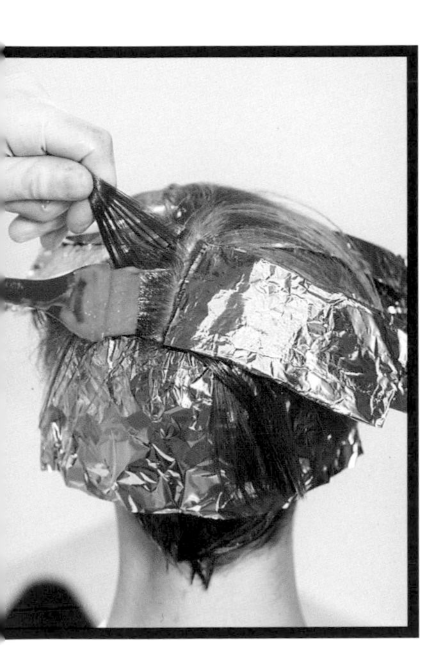

TEN

As you reach the crown area, pivot the sections so they lie vertically.

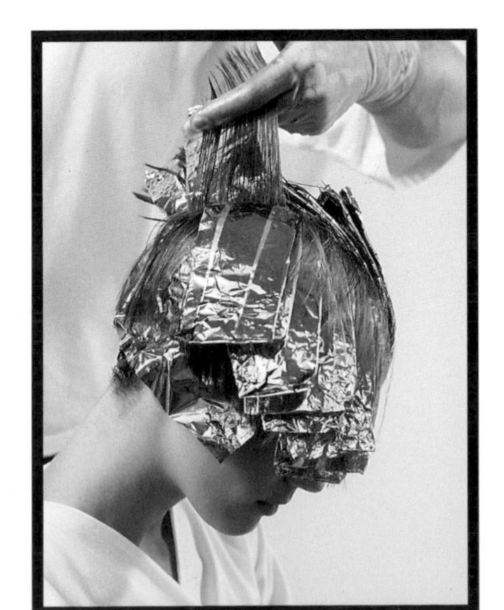

ELEVEN

Finally tint all of the natural hair left between the foil sections using the same tint as you used for the perimeter hair: a hazel brown, depth or level 8 with 9% oxidant.

TWELVE

When complete, process the colours according to the manufacturer's instructions.

THIRTEEN

The finished look: a striking blend of refreshingly lively tones, coupled with a rich base colour.

Orbit with Dappling Colour, another striking contemporary classic from Vidal Sassoon.

NATURAL EFFECTS with INSIDE OUT FOIL COLOUR

A stylish and versatile cut which can be worn in a variety of ways. The technique combines different forms of layering creating a shape that can be adapted onto many varying lengths and textures of hair. Remember, with Vidal Sassoon what matters is the <u>way</u> the hair is cut, not just the shape created.

ONE

Start by putting in a low side parting. This establishes the balance of the shape.

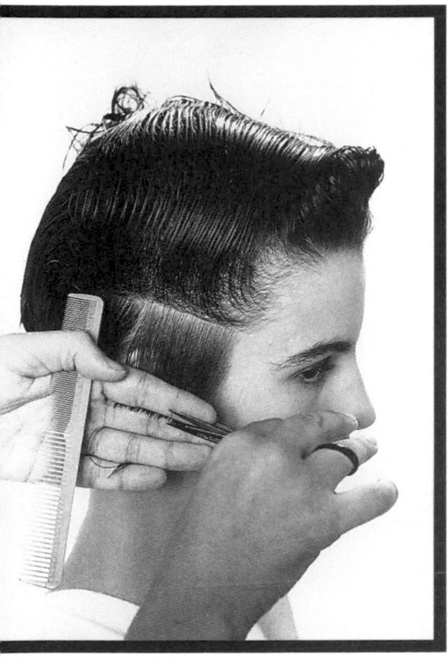

TWO

Beginning on the heavy side of the parting, take a horizontal section from the front hairline to a point above the car. Comb the rest of the hair out of the way and cut a square line, lifting slightly away from the head to create a soft outline.

Now take parallel sections, and comb the hair down onto the original guideline.

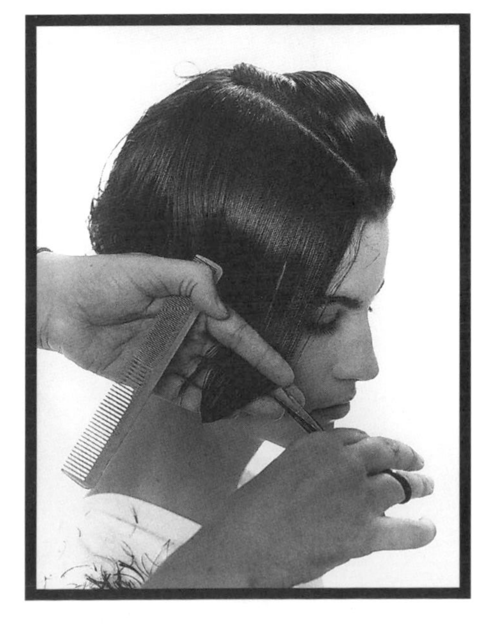

THREE

When including the front, comb the hair over to the side and angle your fingers downwards to keep the line square. Continue up to your parting, taking parallel sections, and always remembering to comb the hair down on to the guideline.

FOUR

When all of the sections have been completed, comb the hair down to check the line, and remove any excess graduation if necessary.

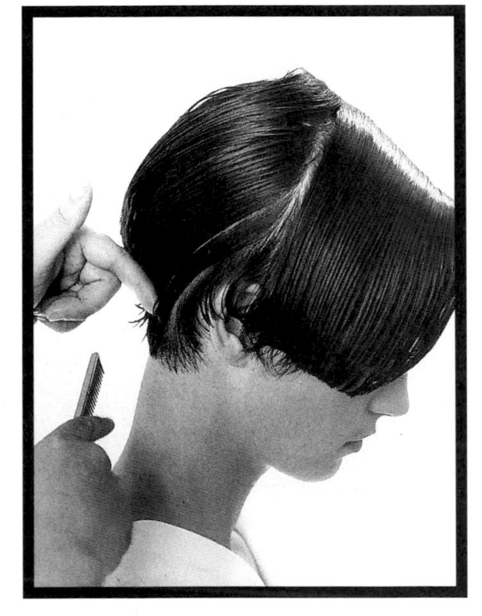

FIVE

Now continue the line into the back area. Divide the hair and take a diagonal section from the back of the ear into the nape hairline.

SIX

Comb the hair slightly forward lifting the section a finger's width away from the skin. Using the hair over the ears as a guide, cut a line angling towards the nape. Continue to take parallel sections and direct these down onto the original guideline until either all the back sections are cut, or you run out of hair.

SEVEN

Now for the internal shape. Take a vertical section from the top parting, down to the centre of the ear. To maintain weight in the outline allow some of the hair to drop out, and then cut a square line above it by lifting the section straight out from the head where the head rounds off.
Direct the hair across and out to keep weight on the top. Take the next section parallel to the first, moving towards the front: lift the hair straight out and cut to the previous guideline.
At the temple area start to overdirect the front sections back onto the previous ones making sure the outline is maintained. This retains length at the front.
N.B. Check constantly for visual balance.

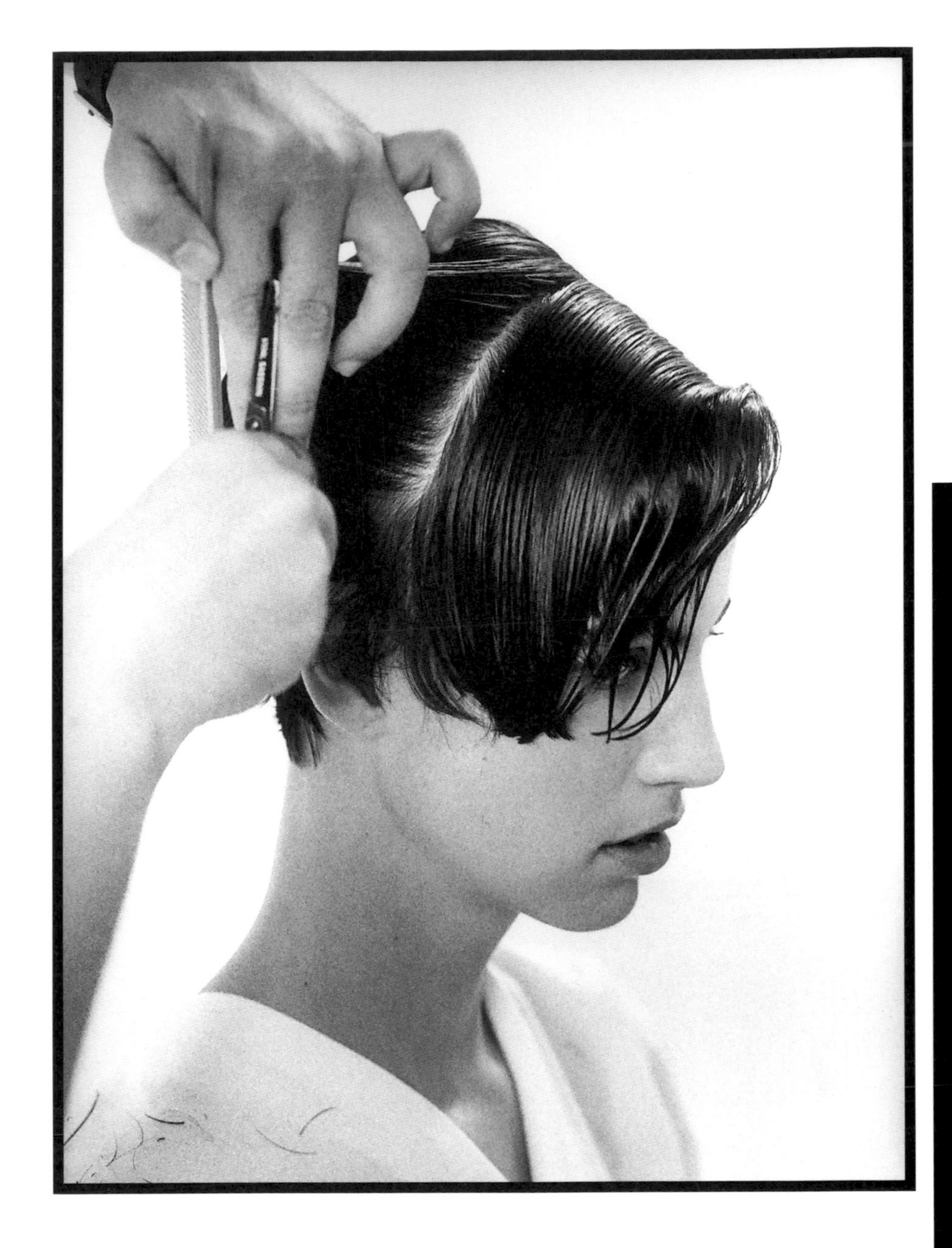

EIGHT

Move to the back area using the section over the ears as a guideline. Pull the hair directly out from the head ensuring the top hair is pulled across and out in the same manner as the front.

NINE

Now pivot around the back following the head shape, still lifting the hair straight out as you cut all the hair above the occipital bone. The hair below the occipital bone is left out to be cut later.

Continue past the centre of the back until you reach the low side parting area on the other side. Check again for visual balance.

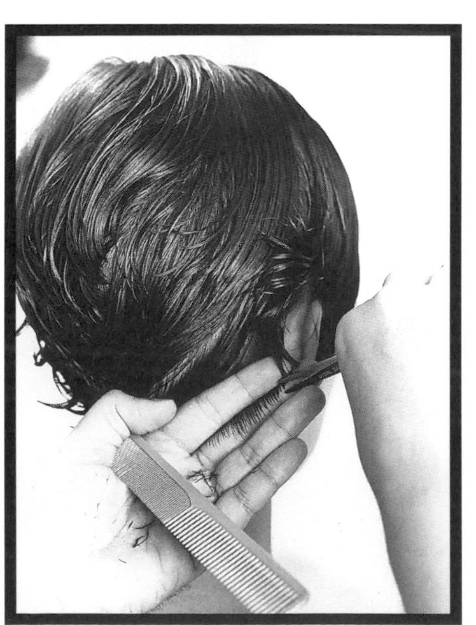

TEN

Now take vertical sections down to the nape of the neck using the previously cut sections as a guide. Angle sections into the hairline at the nape.

ELEVEN

As you work around the head keep checking the shape by combing the hair flat. Continue taking sections past the centre until you reach the lowside parting on the other side.

Refine the outline by pointing into the hairline to create even texture and softness.

TWELVE

Cut 2nd side exactly as 1st: keep the parting in place to retain weight and length on top.

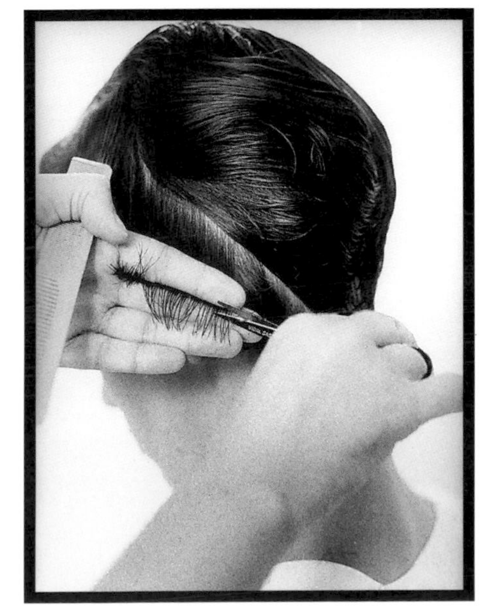

THIRTEEN

Use the 1st side as a guideline and take fine sections so you can see this guideline clearly.

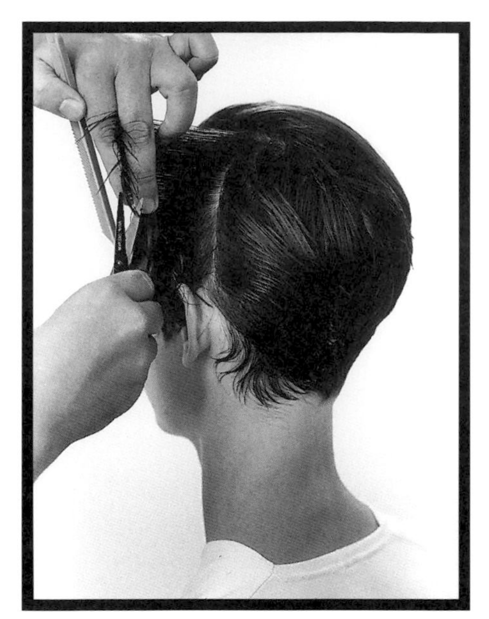

FOURTEEN

N.B. Remember – when layering pull sections straight out from the head overdirect the front sections to retain length.

FIFTEEN

Work around the back until you connect with the first side.

SIXTEEN

Take a vertical section to the nape, angled into hairline, and keep checking the shape.

SEVENTEEN

To refine the internal shape take sections across top of head starting at the crown, and lift sections slightly back rounding the edges of all corners to strengthen the shape. Continue to the fringe removing excess length. Check shape for balance.

EIGHTEEN

Redamp the hair and apply a suitable finishing product.

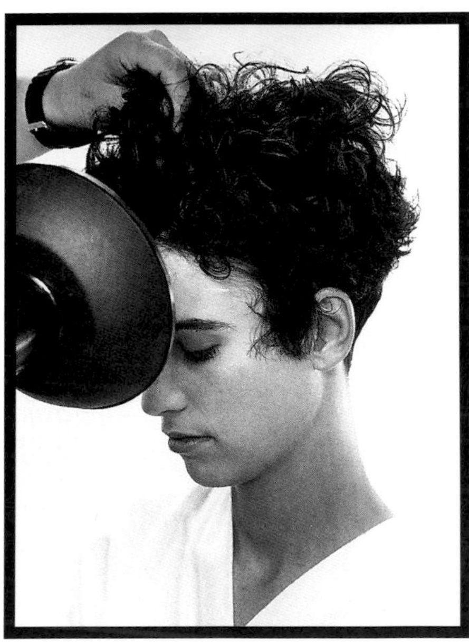

NINETEEN

Dry hair gradually using a diffuser. Allow hair to expand by encouraging it with your fingers.

TWENTY

The finished Natural Effects cut. Because the hair is layered from the outside up a strong internal shape is built up without affecting the lengths required around the outline. This allows Natural Effects to be worn in many different ways.

INSIDE OUT FOIL COLOUR

This stunning technique complements Natural Effects by balancing dark and light tones internally and blending them with a third overall colour.

ONE

Start by using the original parting. Take a small diagonal section across the top. Then weave a highlight section **double** the normal thickness. Apply high lift blonde colour using 12% oxidant.

Wrap in blue foil for easy identification, and seal the foil package as for normal highlights.

TWO

Weave another double-thickness section and apply purple brown tint, depth or level 5 with 6% oxidant. This time use a silver foil.

THREE

Continue taking and weaving diagonal sections, alternating colours until you reach the crown. The sections should follow the shape of the head preventing separation lines appearing when the hair is dressed flat.

FOUR

At the crown, pivot sections so they lie vertically.

FIVE

The completed first side.

SIX

The 2nd side is coloured using the identical technique, once again beginning with a small diagonal section at the front hairline and alternating colours . . .

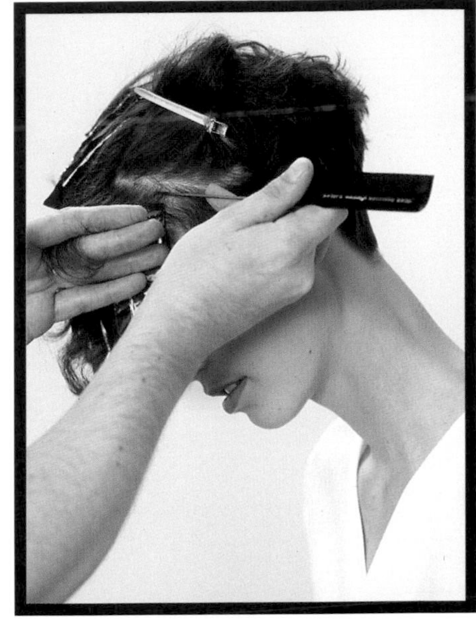

SEVEN

. . . beginning with the high lift blonde . . .

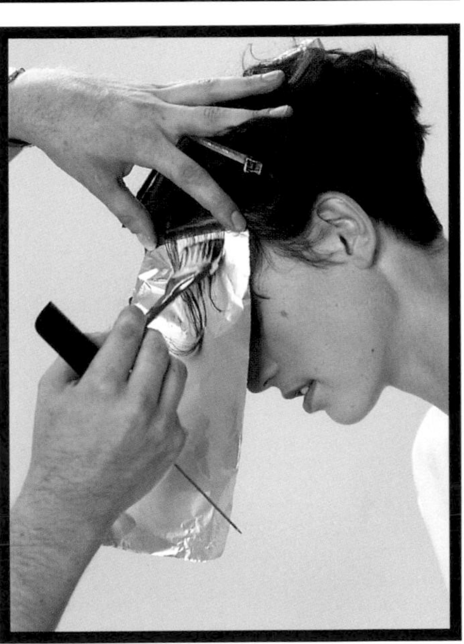

EIGHT

. . . then the purple brown. Continue this to the crown and pivot to connect the two sides.

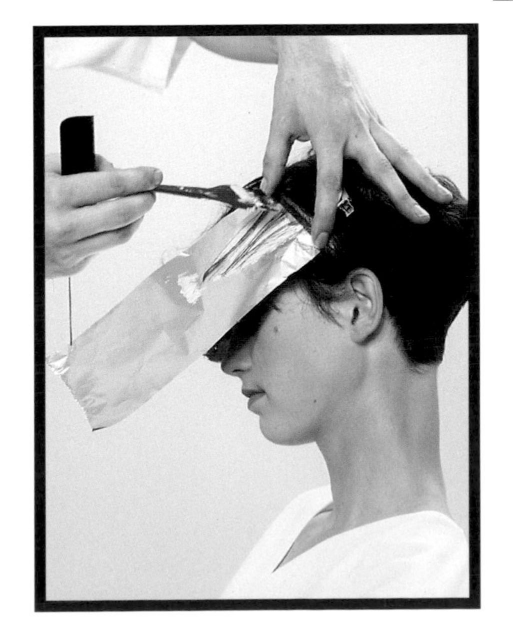

NINE

Process these colours according to the manufacturers' instructions but for HALF the recommended time, before applying the third colour.

TEN

Remove the foils but do not shampoo the colour out yet. This is the key to Inside Out Foil Colour.

ELEVEN

Now apply a soft copper red, level or depth 7 with 9% oxidant. Start at the nape and continue to the front hairline.
Be sure to tint thoroughly over the previously tinted sections.

TWELVE

Comb the hair through to blend the colours. Check your edges and use a stain remover if necessary. Then process according to the manufacturers' instructions, again for HALF the normal recommended time.

THIRTEEN

The finished look: Natural Effects with Inside Out Foil Colour. Suitable for straight or curly hair – a stylish and versatile winner from Vidal Sassoon.

TRIAD PERM

A refreshing combination of a new perming technique with a confident and immensely wearable haircut.

Twist is a short textured haircut which can be created on hair with natural movement or with the addition of a directional perm. Here we begin by showing you the Triad Perm technique.
When a perm is needed to give the required movement and texture to a look, it should be permed first and then cut. Here we will create a soft tousled effect similar to natural hair texture. To make the winding process simpler it is a good idea to layer the hair through before we begin the perm.

ONE

Having shampooed thoroughly, take a parting from ear to ear across the top of the head. Depending on the size of the perm rods to be used, take a further triangular section from the parting to the forehead. Lift the section, apply the perm lotion, and comb in the desired direction so you have hair wound to the roots, and dragged away from the roots within the same section.

N.B. The size of the perm rod determines the amount of texture in the finished perm. Here we use a large size through the whole top area.

N.B. Remember to damp the hair with water when starting the wind: perm lotion is not evenly distributed on dry hair. Postdamp or predamp according to the manufacturer's instructions.

TWO

Take a further triangular section towards the ear. Each section slots into the next one, but lift the hair **in the opposite direction each time** to create different root movement. The sections can be irregular, but must be precise, like a brickwork wind.
N.B. With a Triad section perm you can take as many thin or thick sections as you wish, as they will always fit the human head!

THREE

Section around the ear, pull the hair straight out, and wind to avoid lift around hairline.

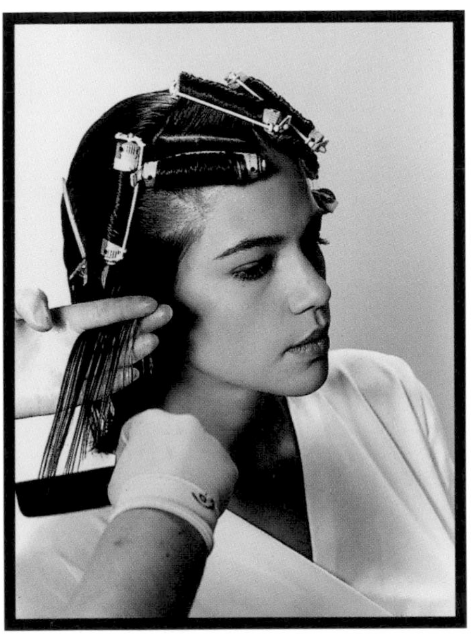

FOUR/FIVE

Repeat the same process for the second side, remembering to change the direction of winding for each perm rod: 1st to left, 2nd to right, and 3rd to the back of each triangular section.

SIX

End papers folded lengthways are threaded through the bands of 2 rods to minimise band marks and to hold rods firmly in place.

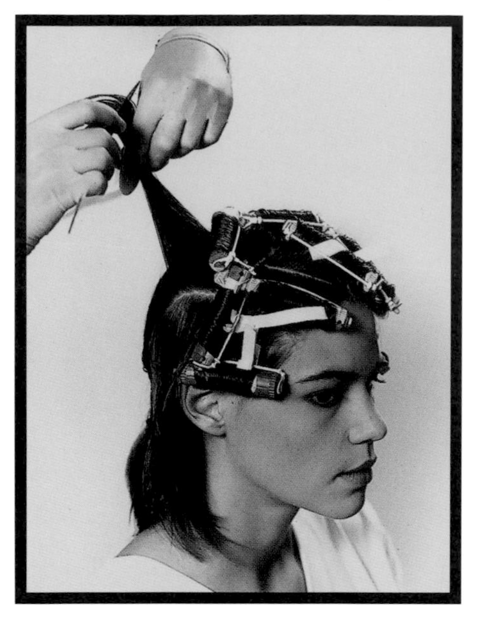

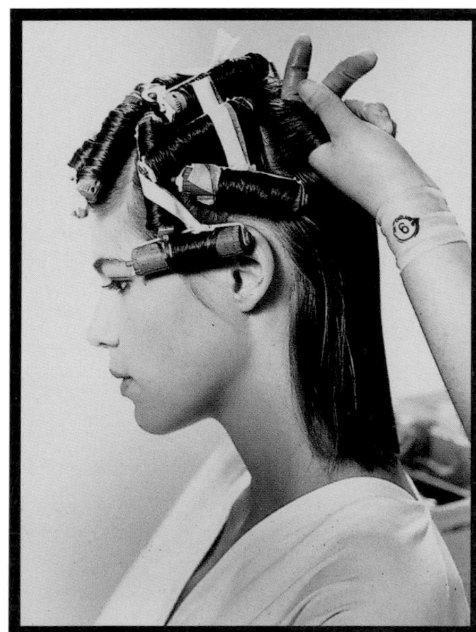

SEVEN
EIGHT
NINE

Having completed the front, take a further section behind the first, of the same thickness. This time the rods are placed in the opposite direction to the 1st row. The last section on the hairline is wound straight out to avoid lift.

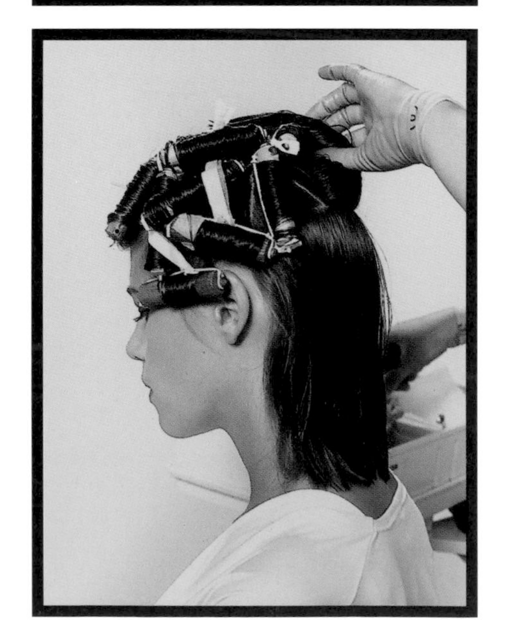

TEN

Then take a main section horizontally across the back of the head, and follow the same sectioning and winding procedures as before. ***N.B. Make sure you predamp the hair with water before applying the perm lotion to each strand.***

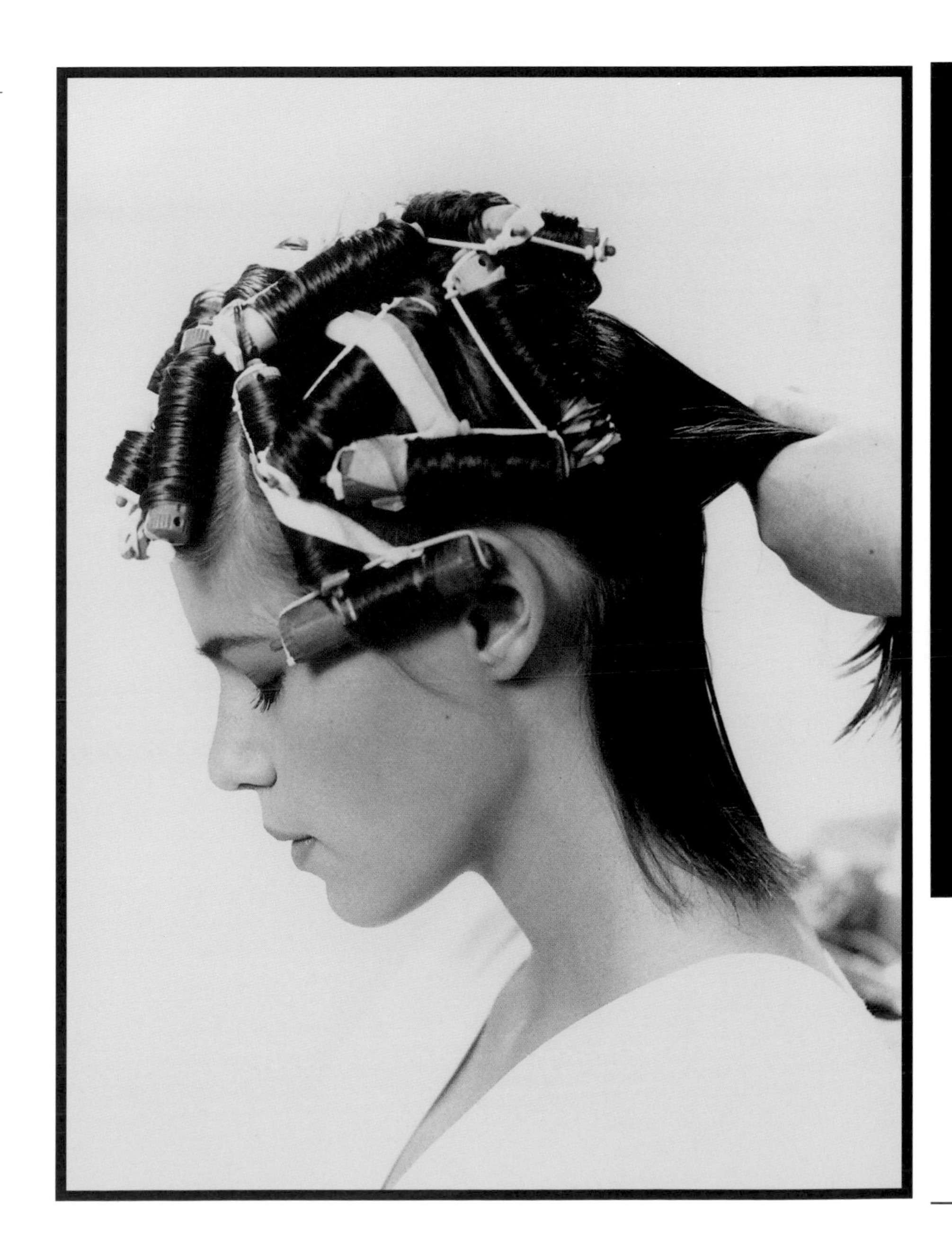

ELEVEN

Continue down to the nape.

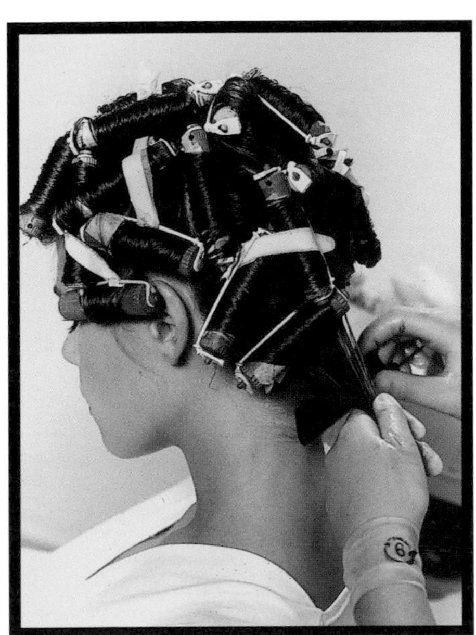

TWELVE

. . . still remembering to lift the hair straight out to prevent lift.

THIRTEEN

Finally apply fresh lotion evenly throughout the hair, and process according to the manufacturer's instructions. Make sure you rinse the hair thoroughly before applying the neutraliser. The end result is soft and tousled, similar in texture to natural hair. This completes the Triad perming sequence.

TWIST

This natural, easily-worn cut combines layering techniques with a freehand finish and can be adapted to many different lengths and textures of hair.

ONE

Start by sectioning across the top of the head from ear to ear.

TWO

Next, take a centre section from crown to front hairline.

THREE

Begin cutting at the top by taking a section and pulling it straight out from the head. Cut, following the contours of the head shape . . .

FOUR

. . . using the pointing technique where the very tips of the scissors give the ends of the hair a varied texture.

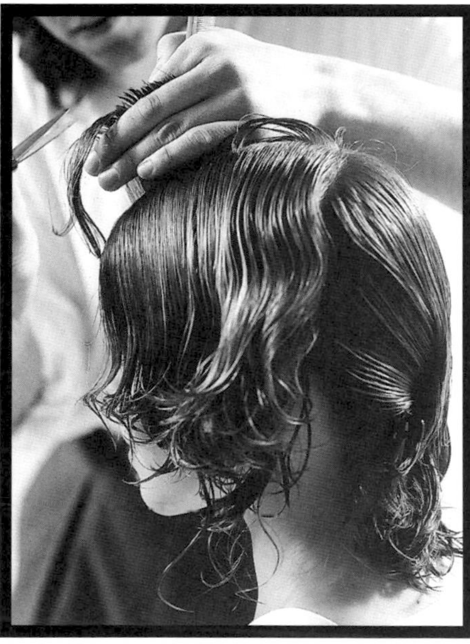

FIVE

Bevel the line down towards the forehead.

SIX

Then take a parallel section and overdirect onto the previous section.

SEVEN

Ensure your sectioning is very clean and precise each time. Precision is the key to any Vidal Sassoon design . . . precision and practice! Keep taking parallel sections to your original centre parting, and overdirect slightly more as the head rounds off in order to retain weight in the temple area. Now repeat the entire process on the other side of the front of the head.

N.B. CHECK the shape visually as you progress.

EIGHT

Side sections are cut using the guideline created by the top section. Take a vertical section, pull it straight out, working down to the top of the ear. Cut a section following the shape of the head, but **avoid angling in too tight**.

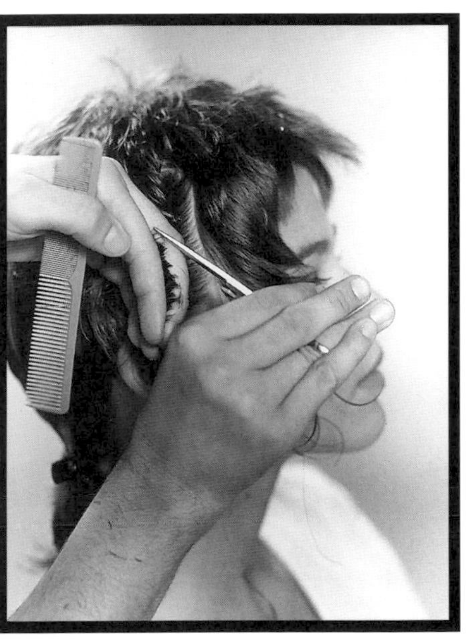

NINE

Continue taking parallel sections from the ear to the front hairline, pointing to add texture.

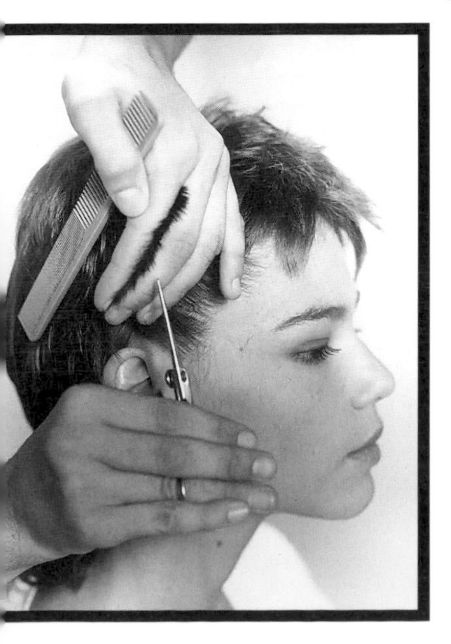

TEN

Through the sideburn take a curved section to leave the outline longer and softer. Overdirect up and out at the temple for the same reason. Then repeat the whole procedure on the other side.

Keep tension even when pointing, and, of course, check the shape continuously.

ELEVEN

So, to the back: take a diagonal section from behind the ear to the nape. Use the side sections as a guideline for length. Lift sections out from the head for extra softness. Again, point in for texture.

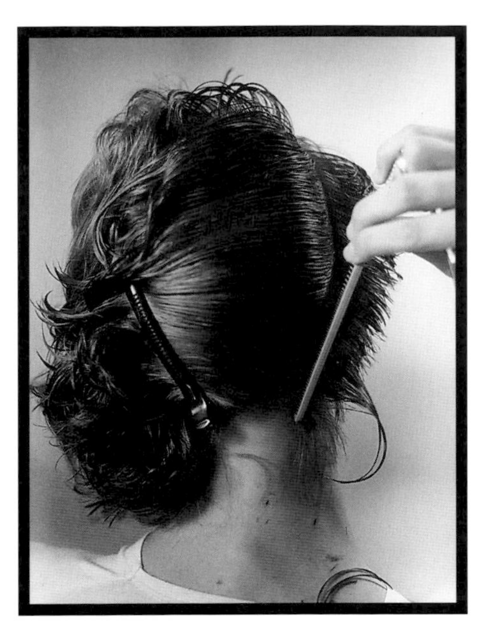

TWELVE

Continue taking parallel sections and overdirect them slightly onto the previously cut guideline. Your line should begin to pivot onto a diagonal plane. Repeat on the other side of the back.

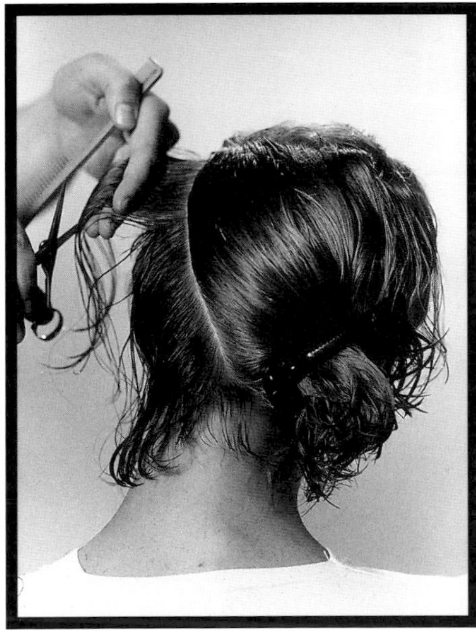

THIRTEEN

The completed nape area, with uncut hair remaining at the centre back.

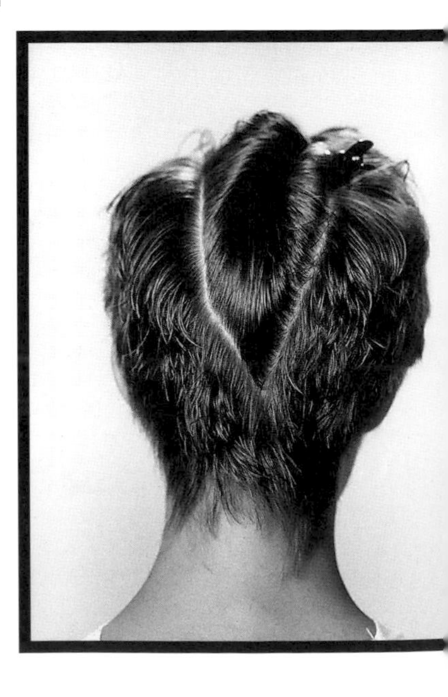

FOURTEEN

Now take a centre section from the crown to the occipital bone, and remove the weight in between, using the crown and nape as a guide. Follow the head shape carefully, and take subsequent sections parallel to the first, and slightly overdirect towards the centre. This will leave the weight where the head rounds off, and compensates for any natural flatness of the head shape.

FIFTEEN

Repeat this cutting and pointing for the other side.

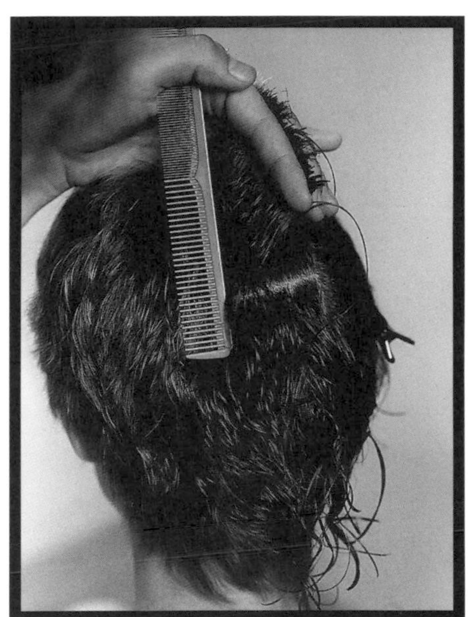

SIXTEEN

. . . and here is the basic cut completed. Check carefully for balance and texture before applying a suitable finishing product.

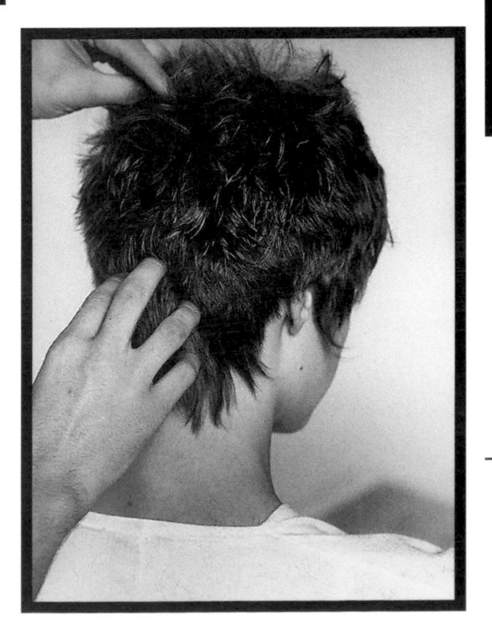

SEVENTEEN

Now for Twist . . . starting at the crown take small sections and twist the hair. Work the scissor blades up the twisted section (from root to tip) being extremely careful not to close them completely! Work in this manner towards the front hairline.

Assess the texture after a couple of sections, and perform some additional pointing in if necessary.

EIGHTEEN

Finally refine the hairline with great delicacy, cutting, pointing, slicing, to achieve the desired effect.

NINETEEN

Twist, with a Triad section perm...another stunning look from Vidal Sassoon which you can achieve with patience and practice.

PURITY

A highly individual look combining bold lines with fluid movement.

This is an exciting yet very versatile haircut, creating and emphasising movement and depth in the hair by layering it from the back, and getting progressively longer towards the face.

ONE

Start by taking a centre parting from the front hairline to the centre nape. Take a slightly diagonal section from the occipital bone across the back of the head. Comb this down and cut a slightly curved line, shorter at the sides and longer at the nape. Then take a second horizontal section and cut this on the previous guideline **using even tension**. Section off the back by taking a section across the crown from ear to ear.

TWO

Continue taking sections following your original guideline.

THREE

In front of the ear take a diagonal section and comb the hair down. Using very little tension cut a freehand diagonal line up to the middle of the ear.

FOUR

Now take sections parallel to the cutting angle and cut to the original guideline. Cut the line upwards and check it the other way to strengthen the shape. Continue as far as the centre parting.

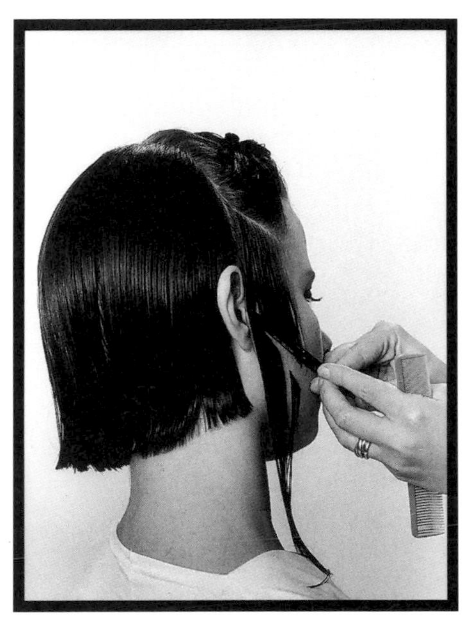

FIVE

Repeat the identical sectioning and cutting process on the second side, always checking for angle and length.

SIX

The outline shape should now be complete. Next take a centre section down the back of the head from the crown to the centre nape.
Take a vertical section starting from the centre and comb the hair straight down.

Cut a vertical line using the length of the outline as your guide.

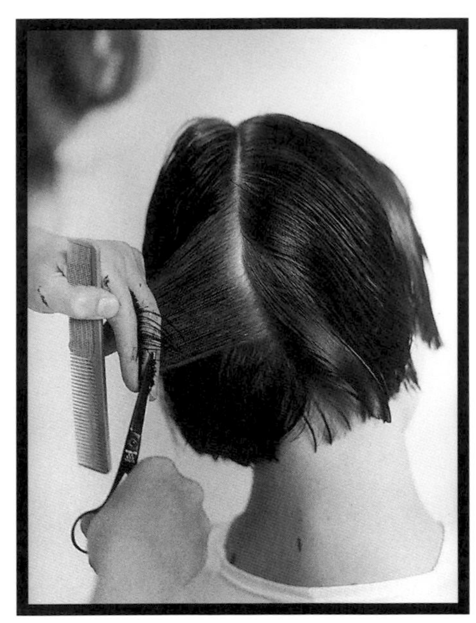

SEVEN

Work the shape square to the head. The second section is taken parallel and overdirected onto the previous central section. When working in the nape area **lift** sections up and out to keep weight in your outline.

EIGHT

Continue taking parallel sections, pulling back onto the previously cut line. Take care to overdirect the nape sections behind the ears back and out to maintain weight in this area.

NINE

Now take vertical sections in front of the ear and direct these back and up. Continue to cut the line square to the head. Work towards the front hairline overdirecting onto the previously cut line.

N.B. Assess the shape visually for length and balance.

TEN

Now repeat this process on the other side. Start from the centre nape, working each section vertically and using the outline as a guide. Cut square to the head and overdirect onto the previously cut sections.

ELEVEN

Work around the head until you reach the front hairline.

TWELVE

In the fringe area take a diagonal section across the front hairline on both sides. Pull the section forward and out, elevating it and cutting a curved line. Join the fringe into the length at the sides, being careful to maintain the same weight through the temple area. Allow the hair to dry off as you cut: this will help you check that the shape and layering are even. Work back towards the crown, overdirecting forward and upwards. Then cut straight across, joining both sides. Continue overdirecting all sections forwards until you run out of hair.
N.B. Now be sure to check the weight and balance.
Cross check your shape by taking horizontal sections. Remove extreme corners, concentrating on the temple areas and behind the ears.
The internal shape is now complete. Point into the hair to refine and achieve a consistently soft outline.

THIRTEEN

Finally redamp the hair, apply a suitable finishing product, and blow dry using a suitable brush. Brush from side to side and from front to back to aid natural root lift. Keep the dryer pointing down for a smooth finish and to emphasise gloss and shine.

FOURTEEN

The finished Purity look: subtle detail complemented by bold lines and fluid movement. Now get ready to add the extra dynamics of Triad colour . . .

TRIAD COLOUR

A stunning technique combining three colours to produce a shimmering effect full of warm tones and soft vibrancy.

ONE

First create and secure a triangular section by taking a centre parting from the crown to the fringe. Next take a diagonal section allowing the fringe to drop out. Last of all take another diagonal section back up to the crown, completing your first triangle.

TWO

Repeat this process as you work around both sides of the centre parting to create further triangles. The very last one should be through the fringe area.
Next work down towards the outline, taking further triangular sections: each section slots into the next one. Sections may be slightly irregular but even so should be placed in a very precise way: attention to detail is key to the success of every Vidal Sassoon technique. Repeat this procedure around to the occipital bone, but leaving the outline and fringe areas alone.

THREE

Now apply your first colour to the nape area using normal application procedure: a red gold tint depth or level 6 with 9% oxidant.

FOUR

Use perm end papers – not as an activator (for which you should use foil) but purely for colour separation. Repeat this on both sides of the nape area and work around the head.

FIVE

For the underneath sections above the ear tint the hairline and separate the colour by placing the end paper on top of the section.

SIX

For the underneath of the fringe use your hand as a shield. Apply an end paper both above and below once tinted.

SEVEN

Repeat this throughout the other side, before unclipping the row of triangular sections through the middle of the head. To these apply your second colour: a red gold tint depth or level 7 with 12% oxidant.

Allow these sections to fall over the previously coloured sections.

EIGHT

Perm end papers prevent the two colours from mixing.

NINE

Work around the head, as before, and finish with the triangle at the front. Finally unclip the top triangles.

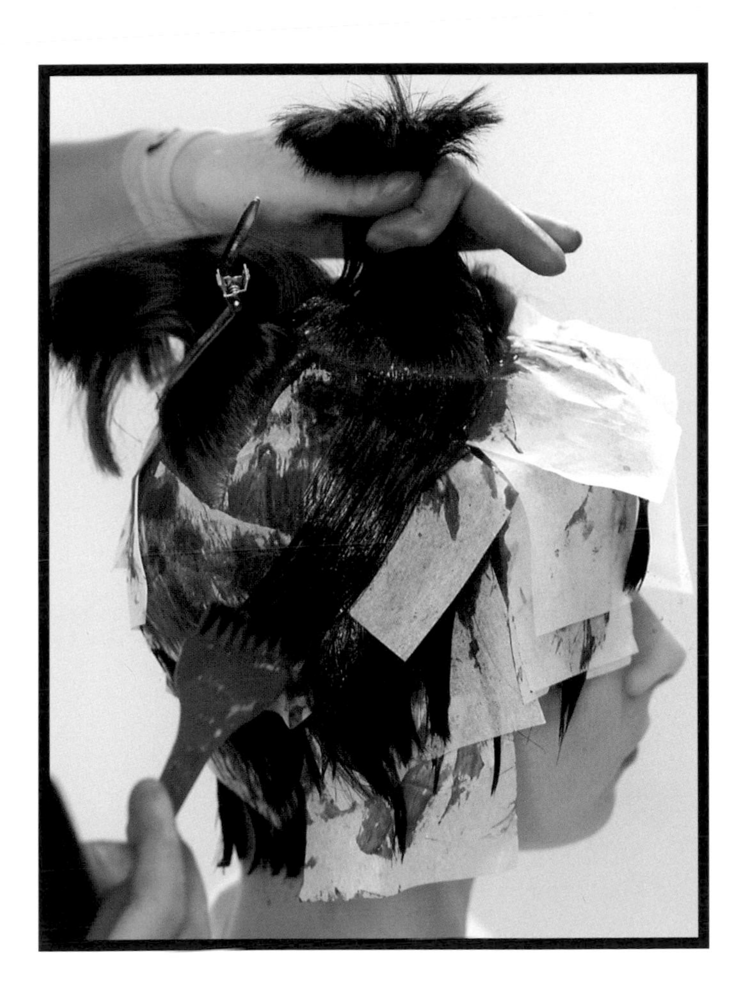

TEN

Colour these with a red orange tint, depth or level 8 with 12% oxidant. Repeat until all the triangles are coloured.

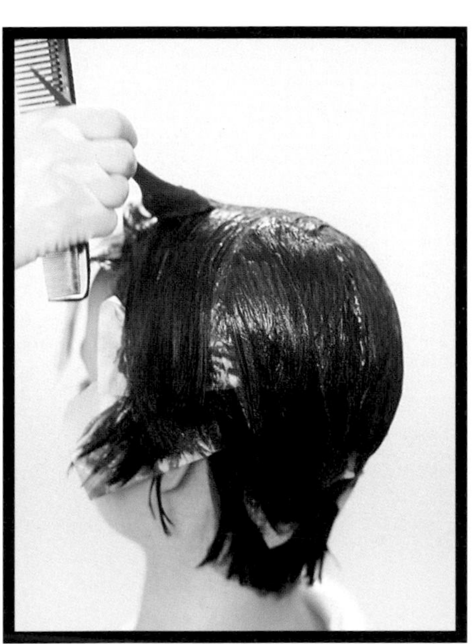

ELEVEN

Now process according to the manufacturer's instructions, shampoo and condition, and blow dry.

TWELVE

Purity with Triad Colour: a striking blend of three shades of colour creating a vibrant red warmth within a simple and stylish shape - another winner from Vidal Sassoon.

PURE ENERGY with FLYING COLOURS

A man's haircut combining precision and freehand cutting, to create a look with defined shape but a loose feel.

ONE

Begin by combing all the hair straight back from the forehead. Then take a vertical section down the centre back from the top of the head to the nape hairline.
Follow this with a vertical section directed back and away from the top.

Angle into the nape, and cut: this achieves a build-up of weight.

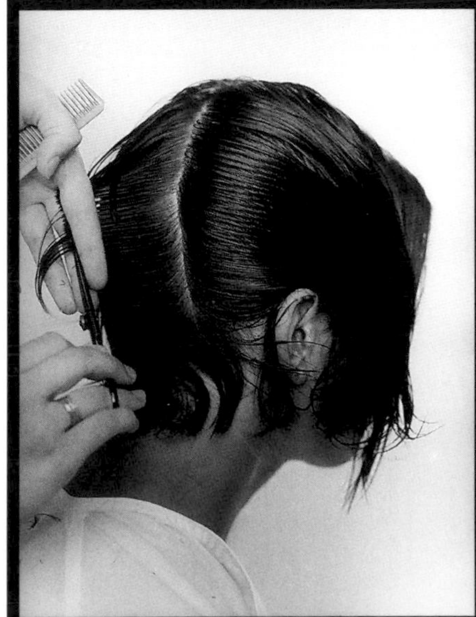

TWO

Your next section should be cut parallel to the first, using the first as a guide. Follow the guideline carefully. Then continue taking vertical sections, cutting at the same angle.

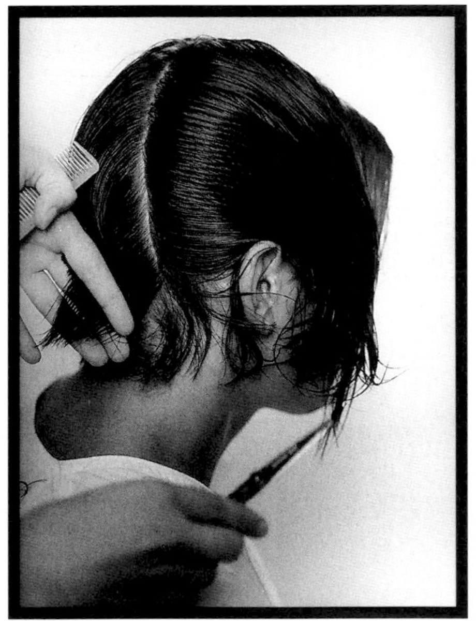

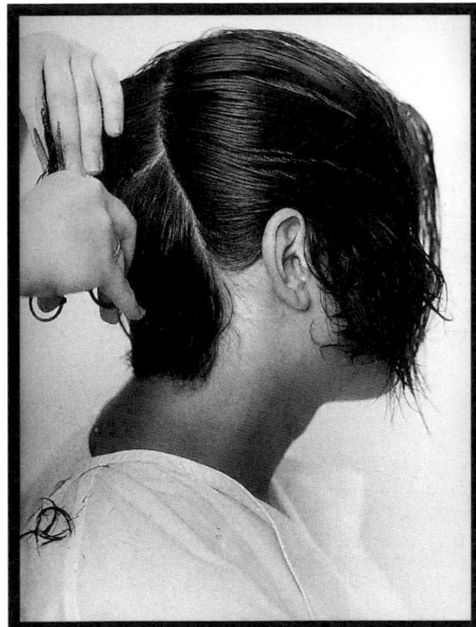

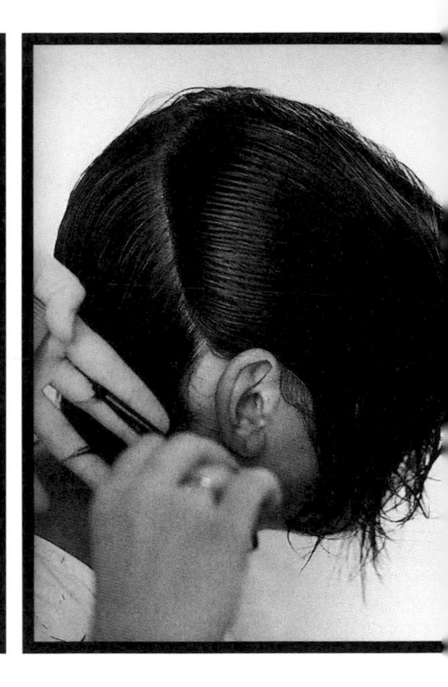

THREE

Remember to keep the hair an even dampness throughout the cut.

FOUR

As you progress towards the point where the head shape rounds off, the sections become more diagonal. Overdirect these back onto your last section: you are building weight here both vertically and horizontally.

FIVE

Continue taking sections, working from the top of the head to behind the ear.

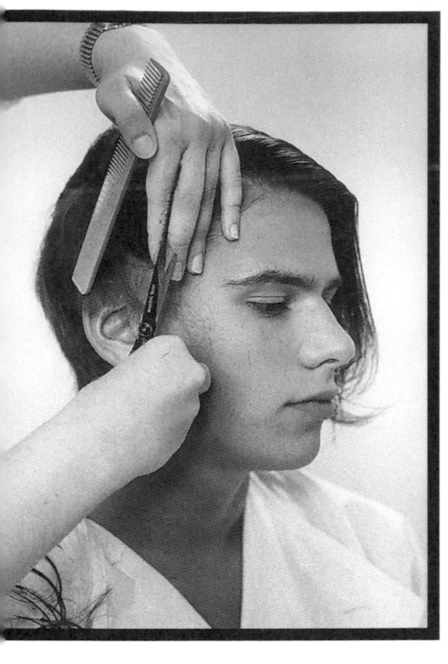

SIX

For the side area start by taking a horizontal section following the line of the temple, leaving out the top hair altogether. Now take the last section from behind the ear, and pull it straight out from the head: this forms the guideline for the sides, which are cut using vertical sections lifting out and angling into the hairline.

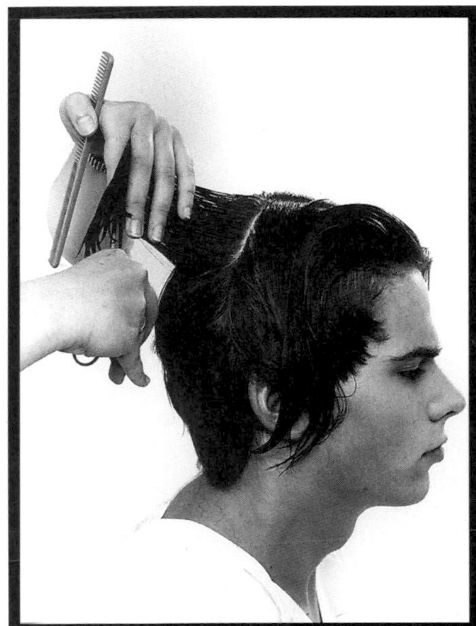

SEVEN

With the back and sides complete, comb all the top hair back, and take a centre parting. Use the existing guideline at the top of the centre back of the head, and cut a vertical section working to behind the ears, and joining in the longer lengths at the top of the head.

N.B. The connection through the top is through the back sections only.

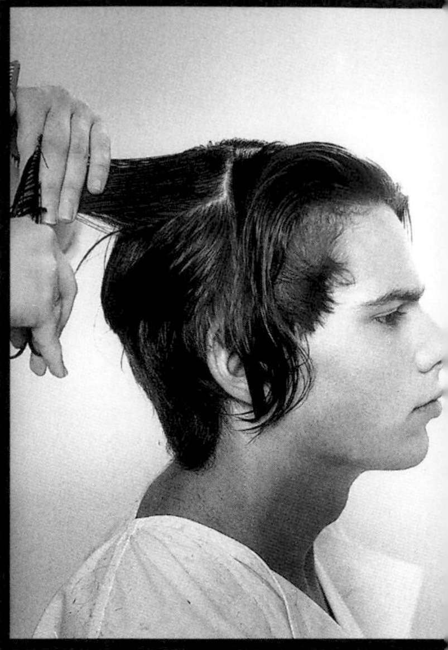

EIGHT/NINE

In front of the ears take a vertical section and overdirect back to behind the ear. Elevate up and out to retain the length through the front. By overdirecting into the previously cut section, where the head rounds off you are achieving a square shape through the back and sides which complements the male bone structure.

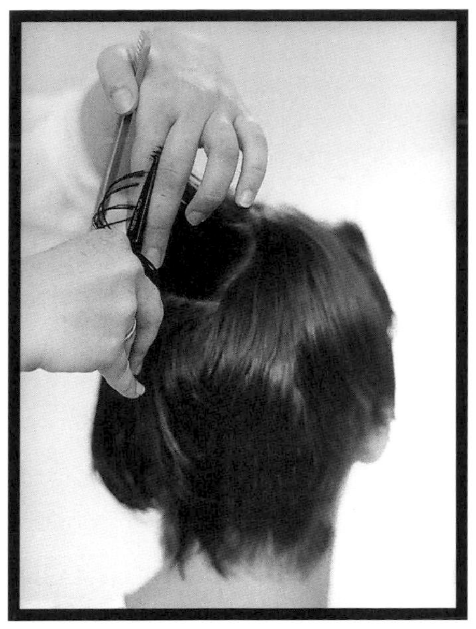

TEN
ELEVEN
TWELVE

Repeat the same sectioning and cutting procedure for the second side, following the guidelines accurately.

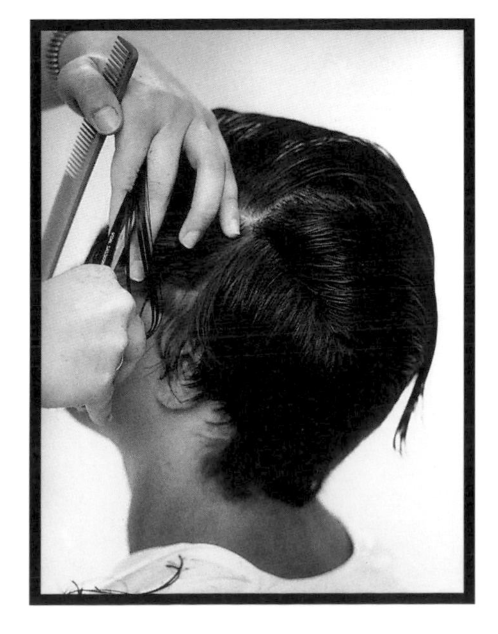

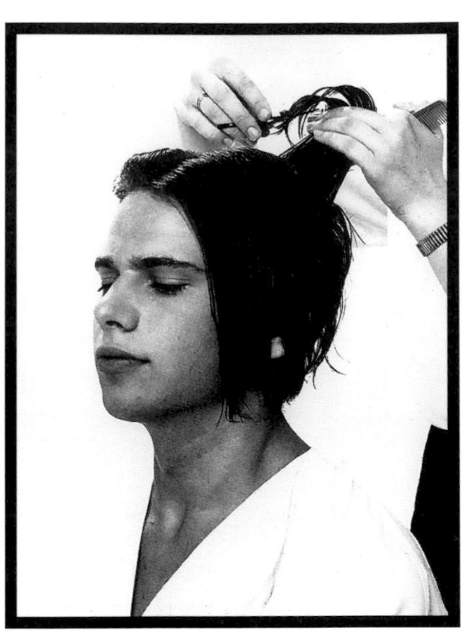

THIRTEEN

The crown section is pulled straight up: the others are pulled back and up, to retain the length through the front.

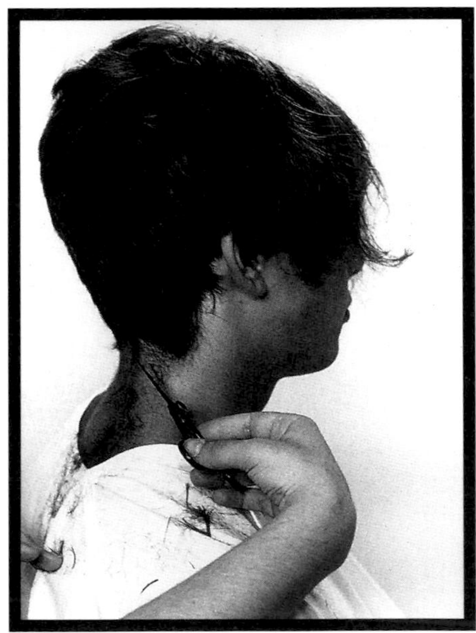

FOURTEEN

Refine the outline using the tips of the scissors, gently pointing the outline shape following the natural hairgrowth patterns. This achieves a looser feel. Work around the outline starting from the nape, until you reach the temple.

FIFTEEN

The finished Pure Energy look, ready for colouring.

X Pure Energy

FLYING COLOURS

A subtle technique giving the impression of varying depths and tones within this masculine cut.

The colours used here are a pastel blonde tint, depth or level 10 with 12% oxidant, and a natural brown tint, depth or level 5 with 6% oxidant . . . but always choose colours that complement the natural tones.

ONE

Apply first the natural brown colour freehand by brushing it across the upper edges of a cutting comb and using a sweeping movement to "paint" the colour on to the top surface of the finished, dressed hair, exactly where you want to see it.

TWO

Be careful not to comb the colour into the root area: place it only on the top and use only gentle strokes.

THREE

The pastel blonde is now applied on the rest of the haircut, working from the front back, following the way the hair has been dressed.

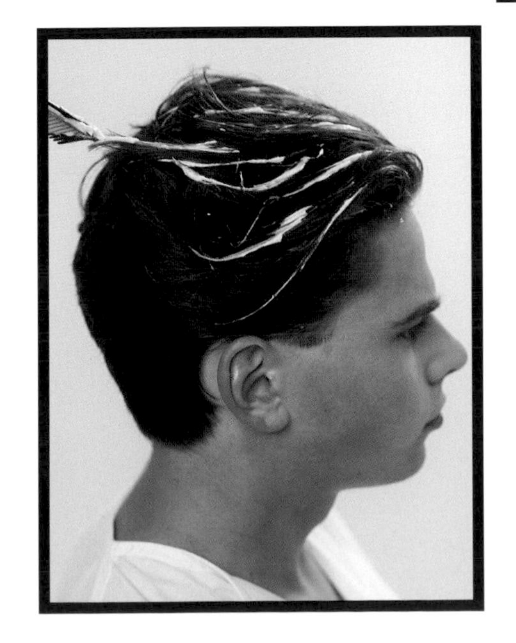

FOUR

Flying Colours is a particularly suitable colouring technique for men's hair, offering the wearer a very natural-looking yet interesting result.

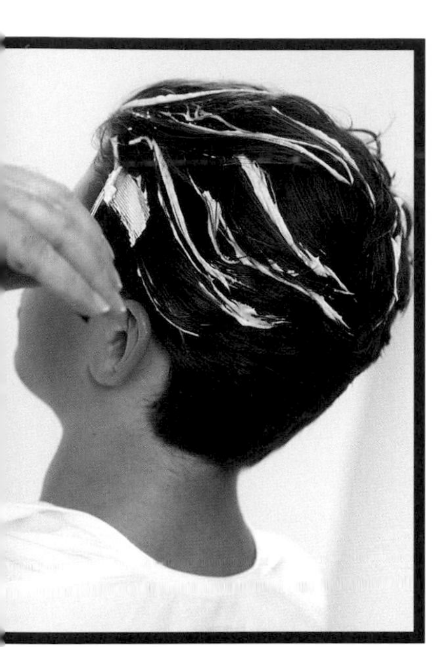

FIVE

Continue applying the first colour as shown, through to the rear of the crown.

SIX

Now apply the second colour in the same manner, in between the light shades already applied: this gives the hair complementary shades of light and dark and enhances its texture.

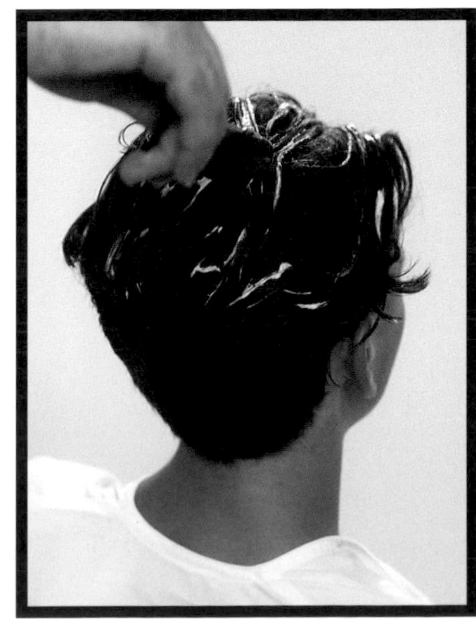

SEVEN

Again, do not comb the colour into the roots. ***N.B. This colouring technique should only be applied to hair that is already cut and finished in the desired shape. If Flying Colours are applied before the haircut most of the colour would be removed during the subsequent cutting process.***

EIGHT

Work back from the front hairline in the direction the hair has been dressed.

NINE

Apply the darker colour lower down to blend in with the natural hair colour underneath. Then process according to the manufacturer's instructions.

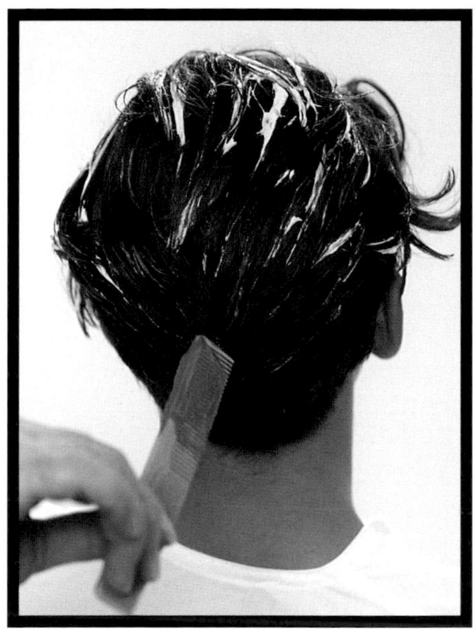

TEN

. . . and here's the finished look: Flying Colours blending and complementing the hair's natural tones, creating a rich feel of light and shade, yet retaining a very masculine appearance . . . and Pure Energy . . . a blend of conventional style and fashionable looseness: a versatile result, tailored to suit each individual wearer.

Two more contemporary classics . . . from Vidal Sassoon.

X Flying Colours

You've Read the Books . . .
. . . Now Study the Videos

For nearly forty years Vidal Sassoon has been the world leader in the art of hairdressing, combining technical expertise and creative innovation in a style that is uniquely Sassoon and uniquely successful.

Now we've advanced the frontiers yet again by creating a completely new series of training videos called, naturally, "Contemporary Classics". All ten of the cutting, colouring and perming techniques featured in Volumes 1 and 2 of "Contemporary Classics" are included, adding an extra dimension to your learning process, and offering an exciting opportunity to see the Vidal Sassoon creative team **in action**.

Essential viewing for any hairdresser, each video explains and demonstrates the cuts and colouring techniques in real time, and forms a complete and comprehensive salon training system. These videotapes are currently available with commentary in English, German, French, Spanish, Portuguese, Italian and Japanese. For further details of prices and how to order them please contact any of the following Vidal Sassoon locations:

UK: Vidal Sassoon
School of Hairdressing,
15 Davies Mews,
London W1Y 1AS
United Kingdom.
Tel: (071) 499 8056

USA: Vidal Sassoon Academy,
1222 Third Street Promenade,
Santa Monica,
California 90401
USA.
Tel: (310) 393 0252

CANADA: Vidal Sassoon Education Centre,
37 Avenue Road,
Toronto MSR 2G3
Ontario,
Canada.
Tel: (416) 920 1333

GERMANY: Vidal Sassoon,
Neuer Wall 31,
20354 Hamburg,
Germany.
Tel: (040) 36 35 65

We trust you have found Volume 2 of Contemporary Classics as helpful and informative as you did Volume 1. We are justifiably proud of our reputation as the World's foremost name in hairdressing education – a reputation founded, as we have already said, by **total commitment** to the pursuit of innovative design and technical excellence. Our formula is very simple: at Vidal Sassoon we believe in **sharing** our ideas and methods.

Recently, with the launch of the new Vidal Sassoon Professional Collection, we felt it was time to put these words into action by founding the Vidal Sassoon Professional Hairclub.

This joint venture with Vidal Sassoon Professional Products provides professional hairdressers with the unique opportunity to invest back into their profession through staff training. As a member of the Club you and your staff will enjoy the following benefits:-

Preferential rates on . . .
*Courses at the Vidal Sassoon Schools in London, Manchester, Glasgow, Los Angeles and Toronto.
*Training seminars in your own salon. International Creative Director Tim Hartley and International Technical Director Annie Humphreys are among those available for demonstrations.
*Vidal Sassoon's new series of Contemporary Classics training videos which build into a collection of 10 precision cuts and colouring techniques. For more details please see the next section.
*A wide selection of professional tools and equipment.

Hairclub members will also receive regular Vidal Sassoon newsletters containing the latest up-to-date information about hair trends, styles, products and many other areas of our business.

For further details, and an application form, please contact

Vidal Sassoon Hairclub.
Administration
15, Davies Mews
London
W1Y 1AS
UNITED KINGDOM
Telephone: 071-499 8056
Facsimile: 071-499 2764

Angle:	Position to line to be cut.
Area:	A specific place eg. Nape area.
Artistic:	Stylish, well designed.
Asymmetric:	An unequal yet proportioned balance of weight or length.
Balance (1):	Harmony of design and proportion.
Balance (2):	To match one side with/by/against the other.
Base:	The beginning of something or foundation.
Bevel/Bevelling:	To round off previously cut hair.
Bleach:	To make hair lighter by extracting the pigment.
Blot Dry:	To remove excess moisture from the hair.
Cendré:	A soft tonal blonde.
Complexion:	Colour or look of skin.
Concave:	To create a curved line in direct opposition to the convex nature of the head shape. Centre lengths being shorter, outer lengths being longer.
Continuous section perm:	A method of winding a permanent wave.
Crop:	Mode of cutting or wearing short hair – where hair is cut down to a finger's width and below.
Crown:	The top of the head, the point at which the growth pattern of hair originates.
Definition:	To determine the shape with precision.
Density:	Thickness of texture.
Depth:	Intensity of colour tone.
Depth Level:	How dark or light the natural colour is.
Diffuse (colour):	The blend of two different yet complementary colour tones.
Diffuser:	Dryer attachment which allows hair to be dried by enhancing natural texture.
Disconnected:	Where lengths are not joined by means of a guideline.
Flat (1):	A section of hair which is left square therefore ignoring the head shape.
Flat (2):	To dry with minimal volume.
Gloss:	Lustre.
Glossy:	Smooth and shiny.
Graduation (1):	Sections of hair that gradually get longer the further they go up the head.
Graduation (2):	Graduation is produced by lifting hair away from the head shape. This can create both external and internal shapes dependent upon how high each section is lifted.
Guideline:	Section of hair, cut to give accurate length and angle to subsequent sections.
Hairline:	The outside edge of the hair.
High lift:	A very light blond permanent colour.
Highlight:	Fine pieces of hair that are woven and coloured.
Horizontal:	Across.
Internal:	Inside the outline of the haircut.
Layering:	Holding hair out from the head at a 90° angle.
Lift:	To bring to a higher position.

CONTEMPORARY
CLASSICS

Nape: The area of neck below the occipital bone.

Natural: Hair that falls the way it deserves as dictated by its own root movement.

Neutralise: To fix the curl into the hair so it takes on the shape of the permanent wave roller.

Normal tint application: To apply permanent colour completely covering the hair, thereby removing any traces of original colour.

Occipital bone: The protrusion or "bump" at the back of the head.

One length: Where all the sections are cut on the same plane, allowing the hair to fall into its natural growth position.

Outline: The outside of the edge of the shape.

Overdirection: To direct the hair away from the position in which it would naturally fall.

Oxidant: Peroxide which supplies extra oxygen.

Parallel (1): Extended in the same direction and equidistant in all parts.

Parallel (2): Side by side.

Plane: Any flat or level surface.

Pointing: To remove small amounts of hair with the tips of the scissors.

Post Damp: To apply permanent wave lotion after the permanent wave has been wound.

Pre Damp: To apply permanent wave lotion to the hair before winding each individual section.

Processing Time: The amount of time a colour or permanent wave lotion is on the hair.

Refine: To add the finishing touches after visual evaluation.

Section: The portion of hair to be cut.

Slice: A very fine unbroken section of hair, which is coloured.

Slice/Slicing: To cut hair by moving the scissors down the hair shaft without completely closing the blades.

Symmetric: An equal balance of weight or length.

Tapering: Gradually becoming smaller towards one end.

Technical: Structured and precise method of achieving a result.

Temple: The flat portion of either side of the head above the cheek-bone.

Tension: The degree of stress placed on the hair.

Texture: The type of natural movement and consistency/structure of hair.

Three Dimensional: The total shape from all angles, length, breadth and thickness.

Tone: Harmony of general effect of colour.

Uniform: Even and balanced in appearance.

Vertical: Upright sections.

Visual: To appraise with the eyes.

Volume: The amount of fullness.

Weight: Areas left heavier than others or pieces of hair not checked in.

Weightline: A band or edge of heaviness in a haircut.